"Jessica Pettitt offers a candid, informative, and interactive way to address issues of social justice and inclusion. *Notice Notes* offers real life practical skills and competencies that give the readers a better understanding of how their own actions and inactions lead to a more authentic way of being. If you are looking for a tool that provides ongoing personal reflection of the most pressing issues of our time, then *Notice Notes* is a great step in the right direction."

Dr. Maura Cullen, author of *35 Dumb Things Well-Intended People Say: Surprising Things We Say That Widen the Diversity Gap*

D1193758

Notice Notes

A Reflection Journal

Compiled by:
Jessica Pettitt

This Journal belongs to:

Table of Contents

Foreword vii

Acknowledgements..xi

Note to Reader..xiii

Be the Change You Want To Be.............................1

Weekly Reflection Journal 26

Next Week...130

Endnotes 134

About the Author 137

www.sjti.org

For suggested readings, visit:
http://sjti.org/suggested_reading.html

the opportunity to deconstruct and create ourselves in our identities.

I use the words and phrases allows, can be, and have the opportunity. I do so because, bottom line, we have choice in our learning and our lives. We can remain in our own status quo. This place of complacency is familiar and comfortable. I find myself at this place in my identities that hold power when my ego is involved or when I'm tired. On the other hand, we can choose to learn, stretch, and grow. This choice compels us to be in discomfort, challenges our thoughts and feelings, and ultimately transform. I choose to be at this challenging place to be congruent with my values. It is not always easy, fun, or popular, but it is where work is done to create change in ourselves to then ripple to those around us. This place is powerful, honest, and rewarding. This choice provides the space for me to succeed and fail while learning in and from everything and everyone, otherwise known as life.

Notice Notes is a tool and a gift for reflection, growth, and transformation. It provides a medium to focus on real life situations and ways to relate to the situations. As with any learning opportunity, it is up to you to the degree of time and energy you put into the experience. My hope is you stick with it—lean into discomfort, dig deep inside yourself, connect your head and heart, and take action accordingly.

becky martinez, ed.d.
Infinity Martinez Consulting
www.InfinityMartinez.com

Acknowledgements

I would like to extend a grateful and inspired thank you to many folks who have supported me through my journey. It is my greatest expectation and hope that you know who you are.

It is with the support of my chosen family that I am who I am.

Thank you, Loren, for your undying unwavering support. You make Elvis' dad proud.

Thank you TTodd Masman for editing, Lily Henson for layout and design and creating the branding image for I am... Social Justice, and becky martinez for tough conversation in Mickey Mouse hotel rooms.

Thank you to the kind folks at Expert Publishing– I look forward to working with you again!

I would like to thank the Social Justice Training Institute (SJTI) Listserv community for assistance, support, and learning opportunities yet to come.

I also need to thank Maura Cullen, Jamie Washington, Kathy Obear, and Vernon Wall, the founders of SJTI, for providing me a space to begin my own work as a white woman doing anti-racism work. I hold myself responsible for the work I did in that space and the work I continue to do.

Ten percent of all proceeds from the sales of *Notice Notes* will be given to the Social Justice Training Institute, Inc. (SJTI), a 501(c)(3) organization, to continue and support the work done in the professional institutes, student experiences, drive-in trainings, and other community initiatives. To register for the next SJTI student and professional institutes, visit www.sjti.org.

Notice Notes is designed for the reader to take one week at a time. If you need support along your journey, please feel free to contact me for a helping hand, listening ear, or even a virtual or physical hug. If you have observations that you would like to share for future editions of *Notice Notes,* please send an email to contactme@iamsocialjustice.com. To continue the conversation, visit www.iamsocialjustice.com or call (917) 543-0966.

Know that we are doing the best we can with what we have—everyone is doing the best they can with what they have. Provide yourself and others with this humanity. That is what gets me out of bed each morning.

Always,

Jessica Pettitt

Jess

Be the Change You Want To Be

I should first start out by saying that I am not a diversity trainer. I am a social justice advocate. What this means is I make people very uncomfortable. See, diversity trainings, to me, are all about comfort. Maybe you watch a film with subtitles, go to a new place, or eat food that might give you gas; either way, you end up going home, back to what makes you comfortable. To do social justice work is to make yourself uncomfortable on purpose and often. So, my goal is to make you as uncomfortable as possible. And I should warn you, I am very good at my job. If you leave this book feeling comfortable, it is your own fault.

Now, with that said, let's talk about being the change you want to be. You may be familiar with the quote "Be the change you want to see in the world." Gandhi didn't actually say this; we simplified the quote, but either way, I don't think seeing change is enough. I think you have to *be* the change. I can see change while sitting on my couch, but to *be* change,

I am going to have to get up and do something—take an active role in actually being the change I want. This is why I call this work "Be the change you want to be."

I also need to state this book isn't a diversity training tool. I leave diversity trainings convinced that I have to stop making judgments and assumptions and read more books, see more films, and then, only then, can I be a better person to make the world better. This is B.S. I say this with great confidence because we all make judgments and assumptions. Sometimes we do this and we are wrong. Sometimes we judge or assume things and we are right based on our life experiences or just dumb luck. Sometimes we have to interpret a given situation or person and judge how much of our sense of self gets to show up so that we feel safe. For example, there may be some situations where talking about faith or politics is welcome and others where this might not be appropriate. I might make an assumption and bring up different discussion topics with other people. Sometimes, someone else may bring up a personal viewpoint on a touchy subject and there isn't any backlash—so I might determine that it is acceptable to talk about my views. Judgments and assumptions happen.

To do social justice work, you have to figure out what you judge and assume, why you judge and assume those things, and if you want to keep those frameworks or retrain yourself based on new information or experiences. Social justice is figuring out how you show up in the world, to other people, and to yourself.

Take a look at how routine making judgments and assumptions has become in our lives. We take in experiences and judge others based on them. We also assume things about others and our own feelings and behaviors. Yeah, we might be right and wrong, or we might just be making assumptions to feel safe.

The first step of social justice work is admitting that we each actively take part in judging and assuming things. Diversity trainers may argue with this point. If that voice inside of your head is arguing—oh, wait, you don't know about the voice in your head? Take a moment and introduce yourself to it. Now we can continue. The voice in your head is well trained that assuming is bad. It may be bad sometimes, but not necessarily always, and the fact of the matter is we still do it and we do it a lot.

Take waiting tables. I waited tables all through college at a restaurant known for its quick, good lunches. So one day I turn into my section during lunch rush, and there it is, my worst nightmare. A table of eight white women. I immediately turn around and return to the table with a pitcher of Diet Coke, ramekins of lemons and limes, straws, automatically split the check, and bring a calculator because someone is going to have divided a nickel by eight. Now I'm not saying this nightmare scenario applies to every table of white women at lunch, but it is a good starting point when your income is dependent on tips.

Another example to help you get comfortable with the fact that you, too, judge and assume has to do with dating. When I was single and dating, depending on what I think might be happening, I may or may not shave my legs. I might shave to the knee; I might shave to my earlobes and moisturize every space just in case. It varies. So, if I am sitting at dinner, and my date can't even chew with a closed mouth, all I can think is, *I shaved for this?* I know in that moment that nothing will be happening later so if I shaved, I had done so based on an erroneous assumption.

To do social justice work, one has to first get very real with the fact that to judge and to assume are ways of being in our world. The great thing about this truth is we all do it.

Following a diversity training, I can feel like such a horrible person. I talk myself into being a better person and then fail miserably at the next inappropriate joke. What is great about my take on social justice is that if we are all making judgments and assumptions, then a *great* equalizer is the fact that we are all jerks. Pressure off. We don't have to strive for perfection, just authenticity. If we are all jerks, that is the great equalizer. Now we are out of excuses.

But, But, But

At this point you may be having difficulty embracing the fact that you can be a jerk, or maybe you struggle with giving great social justice leaders room to be jerks. Let's go there. In my world, Mother Theresa, Martin Luther King, Jr., and Gandhi were the kind of social justice leaders that I put on a pedestal. I often measure myself against their reputations and can feel incompetent to say the least, but they had limitations too. For one, none of them finished their work. Not one of them saw the end of hunger, greed, colonization, racism, classism, etc. In fact, these problems still exist as if these leaders hadn't ever done work to begin with. Yet their work still matters, as does mine, as does yours.

Mother Theresa doubted her faith in G*d. We don't hear about this much, but in fact every day she questioned her faith in G*d and this is how she probably had one of the strongest faiths I have ever heard or read about. She questioned authority and then found her path. Don't you think at least one morning, Mother Theresa woke up, hit snooze a couple of times, complained that there were so many hungry faces? If they are hungry today, won't they just be hungry tomorrow? Sure. And she then got back to work.

Martin Luther King, Jr., did great things and made a lot of mistakes. While working with race specifically, he silenced women, gays and lesbians, and others from bringing their struggles into focus. It is from his earlier work that the concept of baby steps towards equality took form—like a bus coming around a corner, stopping, and calling for certain types to get on, and then promising to come back and get others. This doesn't feel good to many and is still used today as an organizing strategy.

It was his own vision shift that included classism to the point that his focus ended with a living wage and the intersection of race and class. He was assassinated gearing up for a march in memory of two garbage truck workers who were killed on the clock, who didn't earn enough money for their funeral expenses. Neither Martin Luther King, Jr., nor his followers have witnessed the end of racism or classism. People still work well below a living wage in this country. And his work still matters.

Gandhi admitted that he made lots of mistakes too. He was riddled with guilt when he realized his leadership led to people's deaths. This lead him towards nonviolent cooperation where he encouraged participants to respect existing rules long enough to change them and not to just throw them out all at once. In his autobiography, he names one thing about his biggest distraction and deterrent from his work. Want to know what that one thing was? Lust. That's right, lust. We don't typically have images of Gandhi having lustful thoughts. This is the best example to demonstrate how we have removed a sense of humanity from these great leaders. If Gandhi is trying to teach his followers and we can't even hear him, there is something wrong with us. We must take these great leaders and others off of pedestals and realize they are human. We are human.

We have a lot more in common with the greats because we, too, are great. We may not be perfect. We may not succeed. And our work still matters.

So now what?

So you are out of excuses; you're a jerk that is full of human error and potential. So what are you to do now? Let's start with showing up. Do you know how *you* show up? There is an important distinction here, because I don't want you to see how others show up. I believe we have made an Olympic sport out of judging others; it is time to get self-reflective and see how *you* show up. To do this, I will give you three tools—tracking, triggers, and listening. I am not giving you answers or even exercises that you can do to sweat the jerk part of how you show up. These tools help you define how you show up. You have to do the work if you want to change how you show up. You won't ever finish the work. You may not even witness results of the work. And your work matters.

Tracking

I first learned about tracking during the Social Justice Training Institute (sjti.org) and have found it to be a key foundational tool I can always go back to when faced with just how big of a jerk I am. Tracking is about observation and objectively noticing—paying attention. This is actually why I created *Notice Notes*.

Tracking is about paying attention to what you do and don't do, say and don't say, etc. For example, I am currently, and have been since 2006, tracking my choice of language. I identify as a nonviolent person, yet I *punch* elevator buttons, *take a stab* at things when trying something new, and *kick butt* when I do a good job. I don't necessarily change my word choices, I just notice. In noticing the language I use daily, I can identify a pattern of violence-based language that is incongruent with how I identify myself. No judgment here, just a pattern I have and continue to pay attention to so I can eventually make more informed choices about what I hadn't been noticing. If self-reflection is too scary or intimidating, pay attention to the music you listen to, movies or television shows you like, etc. Are there patterns there? Who do you say hello to when walking past strangers? Who gets stopped and asked for directions and who doesn't? What race are most heroes? What color hair do bad guys have? Noticing how you act is fun; give it a whirl. Warning, once you start, you may find that you can't stop. Either warn your friends about what you're doing or convince them to start noticing too.

Triggers

In the movie *Finding Nemo,* there's a scene where the fish are trying to get the pebble in the fan and the music is building and building and all of a sudden the blowfish loses it and—poof—it ends up rendered useless. This is the best visual I can give for being triggered.

A trigger can happen at any point in time that results in typically unrelated and overly positive or negative responses that aren't necessarily shared with others. Like when you are out having a good time on a Friday night and the music is good, you're having fun, maybe you have shaved up to your earlobes, and then one of your friends comes up angry and says you have to go home.

I am of the leave-no-friend-behind school, so everyone piles into the car, then finds out what the problem is. Your friend thought an ex was at the club and ruined the evening.

Basically, your friend has issues, and your friend's issues ruined your Friday night. Your friend was triggered. If you were to track these events, if they happen enough, and this friend develops a pattern, you might even find yourself triggered on Friday night in response to your friend's behavior patterns. You might then find yourself reacting to other people that remind you of this friend—this would be a pattern for you to track, as it has become a trigger.

When you find patterns, you have to dig deep to find the roots of those patterns. Remember that your trigger work can only be done by you. In my opinion, it is your moral imperative to do your own work instead of dumping it on your friends, co-workers, etc.

Close friends are helpful here in discovering the roots of patterns. Just as when a close friend notices bad choice patterns and tells you, others know you better than you do at times. Here's an example. After tracking for a long time, it seemed strange to me that I would get defensive, if not combative, when I would interact with a white man in his forties who had big muscles. I first had to pay attention to men who irritated me. In the beginning, I noticed it was men, and then it was a certain type of man. Then I discovered the full pattern.

It took my friends to help uncover that these interactions seemed to have something to do with money. Oh, wait... With a little digging, I discovered my former body builder father, the white guy who was horrible with money—yeah, my father who died in his late forties, yeah, him—we have unresolved issues. Now, don't worry; I have a therapist and all, but it is important for me to find this root because it isn't anyone else's problem to deal with. It is my work. And my work matters.

Listening to Humanity

The last tool is the hardest, I think. I heard a speaker once talk about a piece of inspiration in her life. It had something to do with "listen to others as if they are wise." I didn't realize the power of this statement until I said it to a teacher in North Dakota who immediately responded with "my students wise? Yeah, right!" Then, as noted in a conversation that followed, we both stood there and realized how sad it was that she had such doubt in her students.

Listen to others as if they are wise. By others, I mean everyone. That person you would like blasted off the planet? What can you learn if you put down your weapons? I like to think about my political foes. What would happen to my ability to listen and learn from them if I approached these conversations from a place of respect? I went one step further and really tried to give them and others a sense of humanity by saying "they are doing the best they can with what they have." This space of humanity to them may in turn give me space to be human. If I can listen to others as if they are wise and respect that they, like me, are doing the best with what we've got, then being a jerk isn't the only equalizer, and we rejoin in humanity. Joining together helps end the struggle and that definitely matters.

It's Time

The concepts I offer here are very simple. The work, however, is not easy. If it were easy, more people would be doing it. Take these simple concepts and do the hard work. James Larkin stated during one of his many Irish labor union rights marches, "The great appear great because we are on our knees. Let us rise!" I couldn't agree more. The time has come; it is time to rise.

***

We take in stimulus using our senses. We may touch, taste, hear, smell, or see information as well as use our intuition, gut feelings, past experiences, and ideas to make literal sense. How one makes sense of a situation may vary from time to time, or there may be a favored process of taking in a given experience. This process of sense making is personal and ever changing for some. When using *Notice Notes,* I ask you take information in and then reflect upon how you might make sense of the provided information and why. In the space provided, record your observations or your noticings and reflect on your own experiences to uncover or highlight patterns of reactions, inactions, and actions.

Noticing[1] is an objective recording or acknowledgement of an event free of judgment, explanation, logic, excuses, or reasoning.

Recording your observations can be done in prose, incomplete thoughts, drawings, word mapping, or whatever form you are comfortable using to articulate your observations, both external and internal.

Reflection relies on the observer or noticer to engage in a dialog internally or with others with the purpose of discovering patterns, roots, and ways of showing up.

Privilege is an inherited and/or earned power within a dominant group membership that may not be blameworthy but does come with a degree of responsibility. The socially constructed dominant identity is dependent on the oppression of a/many subordinated identities. Most people have multiple dominant identities. I am white, cisgendered, able bodied, upper class, educated, in my thirties, native English speaker, United States citizen, legally married, and am assumed to be Christian. I have many subordinated identities too, and I am choosing to focus on the group memberships that give me access to many privileges.

It is my belief that undertaking self-reflection from a lens of one's socially constructed dominant identities is a less costly/risky path towards change because that is the actual source of power.

The Absence of Feelings

While developing this reflection journal, I submitted it for review to a great number of colleagues, friends, and fellow social justice advocates, activists, and educators. Several people in my editing circle pointed out that I didn't incorporate my feelings during the offered noticings nor did I record any emotions of others. My immediate response to this was I wanted to be objective. This implies that emotional reactions are somehow subjective. This truth stalled this project for the better part of a year.

I have noticed that of the folks whom I sent drafts of this journal to review, it was only folks of color that reported back the missing element of emotions. Those that I identify as white made no comment of missing emotionality. I don't have a conclusion about this observation—it is just a track of my experience. I have spent the better part of a year trying to notice my emotional reaction to my noticings, and I have uncovered even more patterns. Most importantly, I have developed reflection prompts to help me incorporate both my head and my heart. These I share with you.

Reflection Prompts

When do I feel safe and what do I notice?

When do I feel scared and what do I notice?

When do I feel intimidated (due to something I can sense—or not sense) in a situation where oppression is playing out?

What do I do or not do?

When do I talk too much? Why?

When am I silent? Why?

When do I cry? Why?

Why am I reacting this way?

What would I do/feel if I were one of the people in this noticing?

What would I do/feel if I were yet another person in this noticing?

What variables could change that would elicit different reactions/inactions on my part?

What is the pattern of my noticings?

What do I *not* notice?

Within these patterns, what covers up the root of my feelings?

What experiences do I cover in similar ways?

What do I use as a cover up? Excuse?

Where do I place responsibility?

When do I fix a situation?

When do I confront a situation?

When am I more comfortable confronting injustice?

When am I not?

How do I protect others with my privilege?

Who do I judge?

How do I forgive others?

How do I forgive myself?

What keeps me in the struggle when the end is not in sight?

One day, while living in Tucson, AZ, I went for a bike ride. The ride was beautiful. I noticed the sway of the trees, birds singing, pretty flowers, children playing. Then I turned my bike around to head back home. Out of nowhere, an intense wind was blowing right at me. I struggled to stay on my bike, let alone count chickadees and daffodils. How did I not notice this wind earlier? As I accepted defeat and began to walk my bike, a conversation with my husband made me realize that this was a powerful metaphor for the social justice concept of privilege. Because I rode at first with the wind, everything was comfortable and easy going; it was when I turned around and faced the winds that I struggled.

Privilege is both going with the grain and the actual design of the grain that is followed. While traveling from coast to coast doing keynotes, workshops, and full-day seminars, I encourage folks to pay attention to their own experiences—after all, you can only control yourself. To fight the good fight (as I so oftentimes hear), I have to actively engage my observation skills, to keep objective observation skills sharp—I have to practice.

If starting with self-reflection isn't motivating enough for you, notice and record patterns in the media, at work, in public, etc., until you get comfortable with the practice, then turn inward to start a dialog of self-reflection. Paying attention to your own actions, inactions, and emotions is hard and noticing patterns externally is equally difficult. As the saying says, "it is hard to see the forest from within the trees." One must collect individual instances, like noticing each tree, and then accumulate them into a larger pattern or forest. This exercise is not about honing your judgment skills, self-deprecation, or the judgment of others. Standing on the judgment line will not make social change.

I will take the first step each week by offering you one observation to get your week started. The following reflection journal has fifty-two examples where I notice privilege at play. The first thirteen are from external sources, while the remaining observations are pulled from my friends, a listserv community to which I belong, mainstream media sources, and, most unfortunately, my own feelings, behaviors, responses, and the lack thereof.

I attempt to record the race and gender that I identify of others in the examples. Sometimes, I can't gather enough information. Other times, I am making assumptions, and in a few examples, I was able to actually talk with the individuals and ask how they identify themselves.

As you go through each week, use the blank space to reflect on that week's example I have given you. As your observation skills sharpen, use the blank spaces to record, draw, reflect, etc. on your own observations, externally or internally. Take notes of your noticings. Record your own observations, actions, assumptions, judgments, behaviors, patterns, feelings, inactions, etc., and learn from them. Then review your recordings in search of more patterns. What I have found is my normal mode of operation is to not notice my privilege.

When I start to take note, I notice where and when I do something that is a pattern that I like as well as those patterns I notice that I dislike. What is most important isn't to be error free, but to notice what you determine to be in error and be the change you want to be in the world.

Week 1 Video game *Grand Theft Auto III* encourages players to beat prostitutes to death.[2]

_____

_____

_____

_____

_____

_____

_____

_____

_____

_____

_____

_____

Week 2 JC Penney offered a gift for the kids: *Forward Command Post,* a pre-bombed home, complete with a soldier and an American flag to crown it with. JC Penney also offered a *World Peace Keepers Battle Station.*[3]

_____

_____

_____

_____

_____

_____

_____

_____

_____

Week 3 JDK Products Inc. produced seven *Trash Talkers* dolls that promote stereotypes of several racial and gender groups. Each doll's facial expression, clothing, and spoken phrases mock and deride the people of the community it represents. For example, the dolls *Lee Chan Li* and *Mr. Patel* promote stereotypes of Asian Americans by depicting them with slanted eyes and broken English. The dolls *Elton* and *Marshall* clearly depict the stereotypes of gays in America. The doll *Babs* portrays a stereotypical Jewish-American princess with a purse and shopping bag. The doll *Pimp Daddy* mocks African Americans by wearing heavy gold chains. The doll *Bubba* depicts white males as stereotypical redneck hicks with a TV remote control in one hand and a beer can in the other. Each doll was purposely created on the basis of racial and gender stereotypes, which are perpetuated in America through these products.[4]

_____

_____

Week 4 Gandhi images were used in the January 2003, *Maxim* magazine to illustrate a story titled "Maxim's Kick-Ass Workout." The story called for a "healthy regimen of violent assaults" and urged readers to "teach those pacifists a lesson about aggression." Gandhi was named in the text, and the magazine had earlier used Gandhi as the central focus of another so-called humor piece titled "Oh, Calcutta: Three Reasons to Hate ... Gandhi."[5]

_____

_____

_____

_____

_____

_____

_____

Week 5 July 30, 2004, was the release date for the movie *Harold and Kumar Go to White Castle*. This is the first major movie released with two Asian men (Indian and Korean) playing the lead characters with no portrayals of Asian stereotypes in the Unites States.[6]

_____

_____

_____

_____

_____

_____

_____

_____

_____

Despite their past willingness to air advocacy ads, CBS, UPN, and NBC have refused to run an advertisement for the United Church of Christ (UCC) that promoted inclusion of gays, racial minorities, and people with disabilities because they consider it "too controversial" and "unacceptable for broadcast," according to a UCC press release. The ad depicts bouncers outside a church turning away gay, minority, and disabled parishioners, followed by the text: "Jesus didn't turn people away. Neither do we."[7]

_____

_____

_____

_____

_____

_____

Week 7 Marin County attorney Bill Duane, a long time volunteer for Habitat for Humanity, is uncomfortable that two affordable housing duplexes are slated to be built in his neighborhood in San Francisco, California.[8]

_____

_____

_____

_____

_____

_____

_____

_____

_____

Week 8 *The Princess and the Frog,* set in New Orleans, features the Walt Disney Studio's first black princess released in 2009. Disney introduced its first non-white animated heroine in 1992's *Aladdin,* a Middle Eastern character named Jasmine. Three years later an American Indian princess appeared in *Pocahontas.* The creation of the Chinese heroine from *Mulan* came in 1998. Other Disney princesses are the main characters from *Cinderella, Sleeping Beauty, Snow White and the Seven Dwarfs, Beauty and the Beast,* and *The Little Mermaid.* [9]

_____

_____

_____

_____

_____

_____

Week 9 Billboards in North Carolina in 2005, depicted an individual whose face is covered by a Kufiya (the traditional male headdress in some Arab countries) carrying a hand grenade with what appears to be a blood smear and a driver's license. The billboard also features Arabic letters that were lined up without forming actual words. Additionally, there are two figures in the background wearing military fatigues, black masks, and green bandanas on their heads with what appear to be Arabic words. Superimposed on the images is a caption that reads "Don't License Terrorists, North Carolina!"[10]

_____

_____

_____

_____

_____

Week 10 Adidas created a new sneaker, part of the sports footwear, apparel, and accessories company's Yellow Series, that features a stereotypical caricature with slanted eyes, buck teeth, and bowl haircut with *Fong* written on its back heel.[11]

_____

_____

_____

_____

_____

_____

_____

_____

_____

Week 11 I received a Flash game email link called *Border Patrol*. The object of the game is to shoot immigrants crossing the border. The game states its objective, "to keep them out... at any cost." It starts with the U.S. flag that has a Star of David replacing the fifty stars. The game shows immigrants crossing the border with a sign that reads "Welcome to the U.S. Welfare Office This Way." There are three targets: a "Mexican nationalist," a "drug smuggler," and a pregnant woman with children, labeled as a "breeder."[12]

_____

_____

_____

_____

_____

_____

_____

Week 12 The Council on American-Islamic Relations complained publicly about plans for a commercial it said would have proclaimed a jihad on the U.S. auto market, offering *Fatwa Fridays* with sales representatives giving play swords to children. The statement from the dealership, Dennis Mitsubishi in Columbus [Ohio], said, "A large number of people have contacted us. Lots of them have seen the humor we were trying to convey, but far too many were clearly bothered by it. This was simply an attempt at humor that fell short."[13]

Week 13 Six Muslim scholars were taken off a US Airways flight to Phoenix after a passenger reported overhearing them criticize the U.S. in Iraq and speaking angrily near the gate. The men said they had been praying. The flight's captain ordered the men off the plane, and they were interrogated by the FBI and the Secret Service.[14]

_____

_____

_____

_____

_____

_____

_____

_____

_____

Week 14 While grocery shopping, I, a white woman, realize for the first time there is an ethnic food aisle with dried chilies, soy sauces, and curry powders among other items I purchase regularly.

_____

_____

_____

_____

_____

_____

_____

_____

_____

Week 15 There is a Saturday morning cartoon called *Lunatics Unleashed,* and the mentally ill are regularly portrayed as murderers, stalkers, criminals, and just generally creepy people in TV shows and movies. I often see kids wearing t-shirts that say things like "powered by the voices in my head" and "some days it's not even worth chewing through the restraints" and "are you dancing or is that a side effect of the shock therapy?" Even our language reflects our comfort with making fun of the mentally ill. We use the words crazy, lunatic, manic, psycho, psychotic, schizo, retard, short bus, etc., as put downs or to describe situations or experiences that are bad, stupid, dangerous, and/or out of control.

_____

_____

_____

_____

Week 16 A white woman is driving from San Diego to Tucson and stops to get gas in Yuma, AZ. She fills up her sporty sedan and realizes she has forgotten her wallet. The gas station attendant tells her not to worry about it and to just send a check when she gets home.

_____

_____

_____

_____

_____

_____

_____

_____

_____

Week 17 A large man gets on a Southwest flight. As he is getting to his seat, the flight attendant checks her sheet and loudly announces this passenger has only purchased one seat. She further challenges the other passengers to watch and make sure his seatbelt fastens. The passenger is crying and humiliated and sits down and buckles his seatbelt. The other passengers and the flight attendant immediately look away as if nothing happened, leaving the man in tears.

_____

_____

_____

_____

_____

_____

Week 18 A student from the University of Illinois Urbana-Champaign declares in a social justice training that white students throwing parties in black face is wrong, as it caricatures the experience of black people. She is wearing a Chief Illini shirt. When asked about Native experiences, she says it is okay to use Indian images because they weren't enslaved.

_____

_____

_____

_____

_____

_____

_____

_____

Week 19 A white woman dressed in a business suit returns to a Mexican food restaurant looking for sunglasses she may have left the day before. The woman asks the young Native waitress if she found sunglasses. The waitress replies that nothing was turned in. The woman proceeds to check under all the tables loudly and slowly explaining that the sunglasses are prescription and that they can't be worn by someone else. Finding nothing, the woman storms out to her Subaru sporting a COEXIST bumper sticker.

_____

_____

_____

_____

_____

_____

_____

Week 20 A woman wearing a sari (traditional Indian dress made of long pieces of colorful silk) is standing about fifty people back in an airport security line. She is taken by the elbow and pulled out of line before getting to the front of the line for additional screening.

_____

_____

_____

_____

_____

_____

_____

_____

_____

Week 21 A transman and his wife are cut in front of by a gay male couple during San Francisco PRIDE. The men look back and say, "We are on the way to our PRIDE."

_____

_____

_____

_____

_____

_____

_____

_____

_____

_____

Week 22 A Latino man and I, a white woman, have volunteered to be bumped to the next flight to LaGuardia Airport. He is rerouted via another airline. I am given a hotel, dinner voucher, and upgraded to first class on a flight in the morning.

_____

_____

_____

_____

_____

_____

_____

_____

_____

Week 23

Three people of color are seated at the back of an empty restaurant during lunch. They asked to move closer to the windows, stating it was really dark in the back. The waitress says she can bring over a lamp. They insist on being moved to the window section of a completely empty restaurant. They are eventually moved and it takes forty-five minutes for a waiter to take their order.

_____

_____

_____

_____

_____

_____

_____

Week 24 A white man in a business suit pushes his way through a crowded train station full of families and other passengers waiting for a late arriving commuter train. At the ticketing window, he announces, "I bought my ticket for today; when is my train coming?"

_____

_____

_____

_____

_____

_____

_____

_____

_____

Week 25 A five-year-old boy hears the song "Boys Don't Cry" on the radio and he said, "Boys don't cry, only girls cry." Thirteen years later, the same song was playing on the radio and he says, "Boys don't cry, only girls cry."

_____

_____

_____

_____

_____

_____

_____

_____

_____

Week 26 A man has a seizure while an airplane is landing. The flight attendant makes an announcement for passengers to stay seated until paramedics can get to the ill passenger. Shortly after pulling into the gate, a man in a suit yells for an explanation as to why he can't get off the plane.

_____

_____

_____

_____

_____

_____

_____

_____

_____

Week 27 An older woman is singing and laughing with what appears to be grandchildren as she is being dropped off at an airport. As she says good-bye to relatives, she gets settled into a wheelchair and rolled away by airline staff. After I had gone through security and been at the gate for a while, just before boarding, the same woman is rolled to a corner facing a wall with her back to the seating area. She looked pale and as if she had been crying. She told me she had been physically searched and rolled into an empty hallway and left alone for an hour.

_____

_____

_____

_____

_____

_____

Week 28 A white woman in a t-shirt and jeans gets a boarding pass, gets through security, and onto a plane after saying once that she left her ID at home. She has no identification stating her name.

_____

_____

_____

_____

_____

_____

_____

_____

_____

Week 29 A white woman says to a Spanish speaking busboy, "You need to find a good woman from Peru. Women from Puerto Rico are too bossy for you. Maybe you could volunteer at the hospital at night and meet a custodian to marry."

_____

_____

_____

_____

_____

_____

_____

_____

_____

Week 30 A white woman realizes on her third visit to her OB/GYN doctor that her doctor is black. She hadn't noticed her doctor's race before.

_____

_____

_____

_____

_____

_____

_____

_____

_____

_____

Week 31 At a conference, there are two keynote speakers back to back. An Asian man speaks on trans-racial adoption, and a Latina woman speaks on cross cultural counseling. Both speakers have technical problems with PowerPoint slides. The audience sits through the man's delays. The woman gets heckled by a number of audience members.

_____

_____

_____

_____

_____

_____

_____

_____

Week 32 At an all-women's college, special hours are provided for the Muslim students at the swimming pool.

Week 33 It is pouring rain as a shuttle is dropping off passengers at a rental car office near the airport. I, a white woman with elite travelers' status, am told to stay while other passengers are getting off and running into the building. I am then driven directly to my awaiting rental car. The shuttle driver puts my luggage into the trunk of my rental car. My last name is spelled out on an electronic sign above the elite status car. I drive away without going into the building.

_____

_____

_____

_____

_____

_____

_____

Week 34 A white male workshop presenter is speaking. A white woman raises her hand to be called on as she has a question. Another white man says presenter's name aloud and immediately asks his question, interrupting the speaker before the woman is called on by the presenter.

_____

_____

_____

_____

_____

_____

_____

_____

_____

Week 35 While visiting friends in Ann Arbor, we talk about popping over to Canada for dinner. I am bummed as I forgot my United States passport. I, as a United States citizen with extensive travel experience prior to September 11, 2001, am not used to having to travel with a passport or needing one to cross into Canada or Mexico.

_____

_____

_____

_____

_____

_____

_____

_____

Week 36 No additional or supplemental documentation was needed for me to be added to my husband's insurance after we got married. To file for domestic partnership, I would have had to prove our commitment in five different financial interdependent ways, like the purchase of a home, etc. After three years of legal/ heterosexual marriage, we still wouldn't qualify for most domestic partner programs.

_____

_____

_____

_____

_____

_____

_____

I am at dinner with a white woman and a white transgender man. Her contact lens falls out into her glass of wine. While she checks her other contact lens, I swirl her wine glass looking for the invisible lens. The transman reaches out and takes the wine glass from me and does the same thing. He finds the contact.

_____

_____

_____

_____

_____

_____

_____

_____

Week 38 A transman's insurance claim is denied for his annual pap smear. Insurance has him listed as a male while the hospital submitted the claim with a female gender marker. The nurse says they changed the M to an F out of habit. She says she will make a note in the chart and change it back. The same thing happens the following year.

_____

_____

_____

_____

_____

_____

_____

_____

_____

A family is speaking Bulgarian at the train station saying how confused and lost they are. I, after serving in the Peace Corps, speak Bulgarian. I approach the family, and, in Bulgarian, ask if I can help. In clear English, the father says, "Thank you; we are fine." I offer to help again and the son says they don't speak English. I state again that I am happy to help and the youngest child tells the parents that I am speaking Bulgarian. The family is stunned and apologizes. They say that they have had such a hard time getting people to help them and listen to them since arriving in the U.S. for a family funeral. They laugh that they weren't listening to me just like the Americans never listened to them.

_____

_____

_____

_____

Week 40 I had the same permanent address from 1983–2003, when my father died. I realize this while talking to a graduating high school student who has moved thirteen times since she was in eleventh grade.

_____

_____

_____

_____

_____

_____

_____

_____

_____

Week 41 A black woman professional is asked to cover the duties of her white colleague while the colleague is on a six-month maternity leave. The woman takes on two full-time jobs and is given a verbal token of appreciation and a small one-time bonus (instead of a salary increase). Upon return from maternity leave, the white woman is promoted and the second job responsibilities stay with the black woman. The next year, a white man with less experience is promoted and the black woman is asked to cover his duties in the interim. Now she works three jobs and gets another small one-time bonus and verbal appreciation.

_____

_____

_____

_____

_____

Week 42 A lesbian couple have been together for eight years. One woman is white South African and has overextended her visa by ten years. She recently had surgery via state aid under the assumption that she is homeless due to her lack of documentation. They worry about immigration laws, marriage legalization, and providing health care for each other.

_____

_____

_____

_____

_____

_____

_____

A black man and I are checking into an American Airlines flight. He is first in line. The agent calls for me first, and I point to him saying he is first. The agent helps him and issues him a first class ticket. I am helped and issued a premier status ticket. At the gate, the same agent calls for first class passengers. The same black man gets in line to board. The agent uses the loud speaker to remind passengers that this is for first class boarding only. While making this announcement, the agent reaches for my boarding pass. Again, I encourage the black man to go first, and I wait for premier status boarding.

_____

_____

_____

_____

_____

Week 44 An eighty-eight-year-old white woman shared with me she wouldn't be participating in Halloween this year. When asked why, she told me a story of how much she loves the kids coming to the door. She tells me a story of last year, two Japanese students from the community college came and were so happy and giggly. She said they were excited to participate in an American custom. Then that same night, a carload of Mexicans came with pillowcases to the door, with kids of all ages and even the adults had pillowcases. I asked if they were having fun and she said, "No! They were just stealing candy."

Week 45 While standing on a New York City subway, I am offered a seat and asked when my baby is due. I am not pregnant.

_____

_____

_____

_____

_____

_____

_____

_____

_____

_____

_____

Week 46 During an extended layover, I ask an airport hotel if I can get a room for a few hours to shower and take a nap. The desk attendant pulls my name up and sees I am a preferred guest and immediately gives me a suite for the afternoon at a discounted rate.

_____

_____

_____

_____

_____

_____

_____

_____

_____

Week 47 A white sorority student at the University of Missouri was applying for a leadership position on campus. She thought it would be a good idea to dress as her role model for the interview. So she wore black face, an afro wig, and a pantsuit. When she arrived, she announced that she was dressed as her role model, Oprah Winfrey.

_____

_____

_____

_____

_____

_____

_____

_____

Week 48 A tall, eight-and-a-half-months pregnant black woman gets up in front of an audience of social justice folks and retells stories of when she felt invisible in this space. She asks of the white attendees, "How do you still not see me when I am this big?"

_____

_____

_____

_____

_____

_____

_____

_____

_____

Week 49 My husband is a professor at the local university in a small rural town. A nurse calls the house to get some vital statistics for him while he is at work. I answer and say I am his wife. With no further information, she refers to me as Mrs. Dr. Cannon, and I give her the information she is looking for, ask questions about his medical chart, etc.

_____

_____

_____

_____

_____

_____

_____

Week 50 An African American woman and her white husband go to a dealership to buy a car. The salesman immediately offers to help the white man. The husband points to his wife saying she wants to buy a car. The salesman then says he didn't see her arrive and asks the woman when to expect her husband. The husband says they are together. The woman pays cash for the new car she wanted and continues to bring the car to the dealership for regular maintenance, cleaning, and servicing.

_____

_____

_____

_____

_____

_____

_____

In a cab from an airport to a hotel late at night, the cab driver (black male) tells me that the downtown area, "has gone really bad. No delivery. No pizza. No Chinamen." At a red light, a black man asks for a ride and gets into the passenger seat of the cab. The cab driver then says, "See, it has gotten so bad black men bum rides from other black men."

_____

_____

_____

_____

_____

_____

_____

_____

Week 52 An older white man has never flown on a plane before. Other passengers at the gate tell the gate agent the man stinks. The agents re-book the man on a later flight without talking to him first and escort him to a lounge area where he can shower and is given clothes from the gift shop to wear.

_____

_____

_____

_____

_____

_____

_____

_____

Next week... You have had a year's worth of practice! Congratulations. Continue your own self-reflection. Encourage others to do similar work. This is the only way to work through the inherited privilege of our socially constructed dominant identities. Look forward to future editions of *Notice Notes!*

_____

_____

_____

_____

_____

_____

_____

_____

_____

_____

_____

_____

_____

_____

_____

_____

_____

_____

Notice something? Feel free to email Jess at Jess@iamsocialjustice.com with your own noticings for possible inclusion in future editions of Notice Notes. Submission does not guarantee inclusion and entries may be edited by author.

Endnotes

[1] The concept of Noticing pulls from trainings and readings using terms like Tracking and Panning. The source of these training and readings cite their work as adapted from materials developed by Elsie Y. Cross Associates, Inc. 1994, Delyte Frost, et al., and the Social Justice Leadership Institute's Core Curriculum (www.sjti.org).

[2] *Grand Theft Auto III* is made by Rockstar Games for Sony PlayStation 2. In *Grand Theft Auto III,* the player works for the Mafia, which involves killing police officers and innocent bystanders, stealing cars, and doing drugs. When the player begins to lose his health, he can pick up a prostitute on the street and have sex with her, as indicated by a bouncing car. As a result, the player's health goes up, but his funds go down. Once the hooker exits the car, if the player wants his money back, he can dash after her, beat her to death, and recover the cash. People who have played the game say that the bloody beating is done with a baseball bat that players can feel in their hands through the PlayStation controller. National Organization for Women called for an alert of action on April 22, 2002.

3 http://www3.jcpenney.com/jcp/Products.asp?GrpTyp=PRD &ItemID=05b5baa&RefPa, December 5, 2002 (link no longer works as of this writing)

4 Online Petition located at http://www.petitiononline.com/ dolls, January 6, 2003

5 Days after a story published on Tolerance.org, *Maxim* magazine has announced plans to respond to complaints about a three-page article that included illustrations of a man beating up an image of Mahatma Gandhi. For follow-up article, visit http://www.tolerance.org/news/article_hate .jsp?id=686, January 28, 2003

6 www.HaroldandKumar.com, July 29, 2004

7 http://mediamatters.org/items/200412010005, December 7, 2004

8 http://www.motherjones.com/news/outfront/2007/07/ habitat_for_hipocrisy.html, July 17, 2007

9 http://www.cnn.com/2007/SHOWBIZ/Movies/03/15/disney
   .newprincess.ap/index.html, March 15, 2007

10 The Coalition for a Secure Driver's License is launching a
   new billboard campaign in New Mexico and North Carolina,
   which contains extremely negative and racist images of
   Arabs and Arab cultural symbols. http://capwiz.com/adc/
   issues/alert/?alertid=8301626&type=CU or http://www.secure
   license.org/site/PageServer?pagename=BillboardCampaign
   December 8, 2005, Washington, DC, December 7, 2005

11 http://www.press.adidas.com/en/desktopdefault.aspx/
   tabid-218, April 5, 2006

12 http://www.resist.com/racistgames/playborderpatrol/border
   patrol.htm, April 21, 2006

13 http://www.freerepublic.com/focus/f-news/1707515/posts,
   September 26, 2006

14 http://wcco.com/topstories/local_story_324220237.html,
   November 21, 2006

From the moment you meet Jessica, you know you're in for something that will challenge your mind, inspire your conscience, and invigorate you to pursue change in your community. Nominated twice by *Campus Activities Magazine* for Best Diversity Artist and referred to as the "Margaret Cho" of diversity trainers, Jessica's programs are direct, customized, and highly interactive. Her workshops, seminars, and keynotes don't just leave participants energized, but also inspired and motivated to follow through with action to create change. Jessica uses her take on life to lead participants through a safe, but confrontational, process of examination, self-reflection, and open dialog that is as challenging as it is rewarding.

Remember, you are your best learning and teaching tool. Keep your best tools sharp. Always use the best tools. Trust the process. Listen to yourself. Listen to others. Breathe. Grow.

To order additional copies of this book,
please call (917) 543-0966 or visit
www.jessicapettitt.com/buy.htm.

Ten percent of all proceeds from the sales of *Notice Notes*
will be given to the Social Justice Training Institute, Inc.,
a 501(c)(3) organization, to continue and support the work
done in the professional institutes, student experiences,
drive-in trainings, and other community initiatives.

To learn more about Jessica's workshops,
seminars, and keynotes, please visit:

www.iamsocialjustice.com